MD Dreams

MD Dreams

Practical Advice for Every Stage
from Pre-med to Residency and Beyond

Jarita Hagans, MD

Printed in the United States of America.

First Printing, 2016

ISBN-13: 978-0-9970241-0-4
ISBN-10:   0-9970241-0-0

Project Manager: Tama Harris McPhatter
Cover and Interior Design: TypeWriting

Website: www.mddreams.com

Disclaimer

This book is for information purposes only. It is not intended as individual advice. Website addresses, information, fees and requirements can and do change frequently. You should contact the school or organizations directly for the most up-to-date information. Neither the author nor her publisher guarantee following the steps in this book or using the resources will help you gain admission into medical school. They also cannot ensure that following certain steps will help you pass the required exams or graduate from medical school. Becoming a doctor is a complex process that cannot be predicted or guaranteed.

Contents

Introduction. ix

How to Use This Book x

CHAPTER ONE

In the Beginning. 1

CHAPTER TWO

The College Years 5

CHAPTER THREE

Explore Your Options. 11

CHAPTER FOUR

Apply Yourself 17

CHAPTER 5

This Is a Test…This Is Only a Test 25

CHAPTER 6

What Should I Do If I Don't Get In? 31

CHAPTER 7

A Wide Open Firehose (The First Two Years) 37

CHAPTER 8
  A Hands-on Approach (The Clinical Years) 43

CHAPTER 9
  The Wild Blue Yonder
  (To Residency and Beyond) 47

CHAPTER 10
  Laissez bon Temps Rouler!
  (Let the Good Times Roll!). 55

CHAPTER 11
  "You *Can't* Be the Doctor." 63

CHAPTER 12
  Hope for the Future 67

CHAPTER 13
  Survival Guide (Future Doctor Checklist) 71

CHAPTER 14
  Resources 81

      Books for General Knowledge and Inspiration 82

      Resources for College, Medical School
      and Residency Application and Preparation 82

      Resources for Medical School Rotations. 84

      Resources for New Physicians. 84

      Medical Student Organizations 85

      Research Opportunities .85

      Test Prep 85

CHAPTER 15

Sample Documents. 87

   Sample Cover Letter. 88

   Sample Rèsumè/CV 89

   Sample Personal Statement. 91

Gratitude 93

Introduction

As a family practice doctor who sees patients of all ages, I get a lot of questions from people about my profession. They want to know how I did it, if I like it, what I studied, how long it took and a number of other things. I would love to mentor every person who comes to me, but it's not humanly possible. So this book is just that—a virtual mentor.

Some of this book is my personal story, but it is also a how-to guide. It contains checklists for each stage of the process and a resource guide with helpful books, websites and organizations. It is not a failsafe way to become a doctor, but it is a roadmap. It will show you how to get started and which way to turn.

Blessings to you on your journey,
Doctor Jarita

How to Use This Book

You can read this book cover to cover (I hope you will) or you can go straight to the chapters that interest you. You can also skip to the resources or tip sections.

CHAPTER ONE

In the Beginning

If the truth is told the youth can grow,
can learn to survive until they gain control,
Nobody says you hafta be gangstas,
Read more, learn more, change the globe.

NASIR (NAS) JONES

When I was a child, I was obsessed with animals. I was sure that I wanted to be a veterinarian. When the seam burst in my stuffed animal's stomach, I sewed it closed and told people it was a C-section scar. My mother's father, Henry Harrell, was a farmer in North Carolina. He had all kinds of animals on his farm. He was a pig farmer by trade, but over the years he had chickens, cats, dogs, a cow, a donkey and a goat. There was one winter when I had the great fortune of being there when one of the sows was giving birth. Granddaddy was there overseeing things and corralling the newborn pigs into a cardboard box lined with dried pine needles. It was the dead of winter and they needed to be brought in from the cold. I couldn't believe it when he brought them into the house in a cardboard box and sat them right in the middle of the living room! They had to be handfed with a bottle. I was more than happy to oblige! As the piglets jostled around in their box, vying for position, my thoughts turned to my future. I started to think of human babies and what it would take to deliver them. Could I make a career out of that? Could I possibly be a doctor?

My interest in Science had been peaked early when my parents bought a microscope for my brother. I spent hours examining the samples; a dog's hair, a moth's wing. My parents nurtured that interest and got me into a Science, Math and Technology magnet program for the 6th grade. We learned about ecosystems and amoebas. We did tons of projects and I would have never been exposed to this kind of curriculum in a "regular" school. Our classroom was like a miniature zoo with parakeets, crickets, worms, a chameleon, a guinea pig and several varieties of fish.

I was a shy kid who liked to read more than anything else. When I was twelve, my Aunt Rachel, more affectionately known as Nana or Granny, gave me a book. It was *Think Big* by Dr. Ben Carson. In it, he talked about his upbringing as a poor kid in Detroit and how he overcame many obstacles to become a doctor. He worked hard and rose to become a pediatric neurosurgeon at Johns Hopkins and is now one of the most well-known doctors in the world. That book is probably one of the main reasons I decided to become a doctor. I owe it all to Aunt Rachel, who took an interest in me at such an early age.

> *You never know what kind of impact you can have on the world just by encouraging a child.*

There were a lot of people who encouraged me over the years; countless friends, family members, church members and teachers. There are way too many to name. These are the people that I thought about every time I felt like giving up. No one really tried to discourage me, but a lot of people were curious about the process. People would ask about the years of schooling and shake their heads in disbelief when they found out the length of time it took. My rebuttal was always this: You might as well go for it if it's what you really want to do. You'll be the same age eight years from now, but you won't have done anything. I love this quote from Karen Lamb which says, "A year from now, you will wish you had started today."

CHAPTER TWO

The College Years

I'm so glad I went to Howard U
(and not your school)!
I'm so glad I went to Howard U!
I'm so glad I went to Howard U,
singing glory hallelujah,
woo! I'm so glad!"

UNKNOWN

In 1994, I set foot on Howard University's campus as a naïve seventeen-year-old freshman. My parents helped me move into my dorm, gave me a manila envelope filled with important papers and left. I wanted them to stay longer, maybe cry a little bit. But knowing what I know now, they probably left to keep from crying. I was sheltered as a child and had only been away from my parents during high school summer programs. Luckily, I had been to a pre-freshman summer program at Howard, so I wasn't totally alone. I had a handful of friends and I set out to find them.

All four of us were Biology majors and had set out to become doctors. My New York friend was a short, sassy, caramel colored girl who all the boys loved. I would borrow clothes and shoes from her in an attempt to be fashionable. Our other two friends were from Virginia, one from Franklin and the other from Farmville. My Franklin friend was a thin, brown-skinned girl, with hair so thick and healthy it looked like a wig. She had a photographic memory and would whiz through the chemistry and biology facts that the rest of us struggled over all night long. My Farmville friend was a light-skinned girl with long, thick black hair. She was a homebody who loved sports. She and I became athletic trainers for the football team. We did everything together and are still friends to this day.

The freedom of that first year was amazing! There was no one telling me what to do anymore. I got up when I wanted, ate when I wanted, slept when I wanted and went out when I wanted. I fell in love with my freedom and the whole college experience. I danced to the band at the football games and watched the fraternities and sororities step on the yard. My friends and I clubbed and partied every weekend. I attended talks from famous guest lecturers like Stokely Carmichael, also known as Kwame Toure. He was a Howard grad and had risen through the ranks to become one of the leaders of the Black Panther party. Even the great Nelson Mandela, President of South Africa and warrior against apartheid, spoke at convocation during my freshman year.

Despite all my newfound freedom and extracurricular activities, I still had to get up in the morning. Biology 101 was at eight AM and the professors were not playing, especially Dr. Geraldine Twitty. She unceremoniously informed us that baby school was over and we were just going to have to rise to the occasion. She would stand directly in front of any student who was sleeping and scare them half to death. Then there was the "project" we had to do which basically amounted to a scientific scavenger hunt at the Museum of Natural History. This was four years before the advent of Google, so it was difficult to find certain types of information. I appreciate her now, but definitely struggled through that class.

As a Biology major at Howard, you had a Chemistry minor by default. Chemistry was the bane of my existence. I had to take and pass a certain number of Chemistry classes as a graduation requirement. The first time I took Organic Chemistry, I got a D. It seemed like my mind would just shut down when it saw those equations. I had to take it again in the summer. I had a different professor that time and it was the only thing I had to concentrate on during the summer semester. My study partner was a cute Muslim guy with thick-rimmed glasses and spiky dreads. I had met him in my pre-freshman summer program. We had a lot of free time on our hands, so we would play Jenga and talk for hours while burning incense and listening to the jazz station. This Organic Chemistry class was a different story though. We spent hours in the library after class working out formulas and equations. I think that is what was lacking before. I had spent a lot of time reading the theories and not enough time solving the problems. That's kind of a metaphor for life, isn't it? Sometimes we allow ourselves to get bogged down with researching a particular thing, when it might behoove us to start doing the work.

Sometimes we allow ourselves to get bogged down with researching a particular thing, when it might behoove us to start doing the work.

You don't *really* know if you can do it, until you start doing it.

After getting over the chemistry hurdle, there was nothing in my way on the road to becoming a doctor. All I had to do now was maintain my grades and get some experiences under my belt. I knew two doctors personally. Dr. Smith was a Family Practitioner who attended the church I grew up in. My cousin Junior had gone to Duke and become a Cardiothoracic Surgeon. However, I needed to work with someone directly. I signed up for a shadowing program at Howard University Hospital that was held during a week-long break from school. I was assigned to Dr. Clarke, an Anesthesiologist. I originally wanted to shadow a surgeon, but it ended up being the best thing for me. Dr. Clarke was young, brilliant and apt to teach. I followed him from case to case for each intubation and induction. I also had a bird's eye view of all the surgeries going on. One thing I will never forget is the smell of burning flesh. The surgeon was using electrocautery to stop some of the bleeding in the surgical field. I thought I was going to vomit. The odor was so pungent, I had to leave the room. I have since gotten used to the smell and I have learned how to raise my soft palate to close my nose without pinching it. This comes in handy regularly when patients don't have the most pleasant odor.

The summer after my sophomore year, I did some research with a Molecular Endocrinologist. His work was in erythrocyte insulin binding. I spent the summer helping the graduate students do some benchwork, organizing the lab and pouring over hundreds of journal articles. I was in the library for hours, copying the articles my mentor wanted. It wasn't exciting, but I ended up reading some of those journal articles. Because of that, I was able to ask my mentor some intelligent questions. I did not know it at the time, but Dr. G was on the admissions board at the medical school. This is why you should always do your best work. You never know who is watching. I did not get into medical school the first time I applied and I did not apply to Howard. In my mind, I had wanted to go away for med school and then come back to Howard for residency. When I came back to Dr. G for a letter of recommendation on my second try, he asked if I wanted to go to Howard. My response was, "I want to go wherever I get in." He said that if I wanted to go to Howard, he could make it happen.

CHAPTER THREE

Explore Your Options

Don't ask yourself what the world needs;
ask yourself what makes you come alive.
And then go and do that. Because what the
world needs is people who have come alive.

HOWARD THURMAN

I can't tell you enough times: make sure that this is what you want to do before you start doing it. This road is so long, tedious and expensive. You will not make it if you are not passionate about it. I had a classmate who went through all of the preparation, test-taking, application process, interviewing and the whole first year, before he finally decided that he did not want to be a doctor. You can't be doing this for money, for prestige or because your mommy and daddy want you to. You can't be lukewarm about it. It better be a burning desire.

Before you go down this road, drop what you are doing and go to ExploreHealthCareers.com. It has information on all kinds of health careers: Pharmacy, Veterinary Medicine, Nursing, Nutrition, Physician Assistant, Public Health, Physical Therapy, etc. I am not saying this to try to discourage you; I want you to explore all of your options and find out if this is the career for you before you spend a lot of time and money pursuing it. You may find something else that is a better fit or that you would enjoy more. Spend some time getting clear on what you want to do and why. If you don't know what your purpose and passion are, I encourage you to read Rick Warren's book, *The Purpose Driven Life*. Gary Vaynerchuck, the social media guru, has an amazing book as well. It's called *Crush It. Why Now is the Time to Cash in on Your Passion*. If you don't get excited when you read that, then you're probably dead. You may also want to visit the websites of some thought leaders in this area, such as Jullien Gordon at julliengordon.com and Rosetta Thurman at happyblackwoman.com.

With all that being said, if you still want to do this, you have another choice to make. Allopathic or traditional medical school isn't for everyone. There are plenty of other routes to take to a career in medicine. Podiatrists, chiropractors and dentists are doctors too. You owe it to yourself to look into these careers and find out if there is anything else you are interested in. There is nothing worse than getting deeply invested in something, just to later wish you had taken another route. You'll find some information below to get you started.

The American Association of Colleges of Podiatric Medicine has a pretty comprehensive website at www.aacpm. org. It includes information on all stages (school, residency and career). It has some interesting sections on what a podiatrist does, earning potential, podiatric education, how to apply to school and contacting a mentor.

The Chiropractic College Application Service at portal.chirocas.org is a central application service that not all chiropractic programs participate in. The Frequently Asked

Questions section tells you which schools participate, what to do before you apply and tells you about the application process itself. You would need to contact the schools directly for a list of prerequisites and other admission information.

There is a central application service for most U.S. dental schools that can be found at portal.aadsaweb.org. Again, contact the individual schools for their admissions requirements. The American Dental Association (ADA) has information for high school and college students. Their website, www.ada.org/en/education_careers, also has a section on how to apply, finding a mentor, and dentistry career options. You might also want to pay a visit to the American Dental Education Association's website at www.adea.org. You can find scholarships, tips on preparing to enter dental school, summer programs and other enrichment opportunities there. Click on the "information for prospective students" tab.

Have you heard of a DO? It means Doctor of Osteopathic Medicine. What is it? I'm glad you asked. Osteopathic physicians receive four years of basic medical education and can go into any medical specialty that an MD can. In addition to this, DOs are trained in the musculoskeletal system and osteopathic manipulative treatment (OMT). According to www.osteopathic.org, "…osteopathic physicians use their hands to diagnose illness and injury to encourage your body's natural tendency toward good health." The following websites could be helpful as well: the American Association of Colleges of Osteopathic Medicine at www.aacom.org, and aacomas.aacom.org, a central application service.

You may also want to consider becoming a Nurse Practitioner or a Physician's Assistant. These two careers are sometimes confused or used interchangeably by people who don't know the difference. Nurse Practitioners (NPs) are RNs who receive extra years of training. Once they receive their NP certification, they can see patients, prescribe medicine, and do many of the things your doctor can do. The only caveat is that in some states they must have a collaborating agreement with a physician who periodically reviews their work and is available for consultation. Nurse Practitioners are certified in a particular specialty, like Family Practice or Pediatrics. Right now, the Master of Science in Nursing program takes about three years. In 2015, a Doctor of Nursing Practice (DNP) will be the degree required to become a Nurse Practitioner. Visit www.aanp.org, the American Association of Nurse Practitioners site, and click on the "Education" tab. Scroll down to "Student Resource Center," there you will find out about NP education, scholarship and career info. You can also go to the American Association of Colleges of Nursing website and click on the "Doctor of Nursing Practice" tab.

I can't tell you enough times: make sure that this is what you want to do before you start doing it.

Physician's Assistants (PAs) practice medicine under the supervision of a physician. Examining patients and pre-scribing medicine (with a co-signer) is something they are licensed to do. They are considered physician extenders, and can be a vital member of the healthcare team. Having a PA around allows a medical practice or rounding physician to see more patients than they could do if they were on their own. For example, a Physician's Assistant could take care of the needs of patients on the hospital floors while the doctor they work with is in the operating room or the office. Most schools require two years of college as a prerequisite and the training program itself is about three years. You can find out more about this career at www.aapa.org, the American Academy of Physician Assistants website.

CHAPTER FOUR

Apply Yourself

The question isn't who's going to let me,
it's who's going to stop me.

AYN RAND

Applying to medical school is a lengthy process, but should go smoothly as long as you pay attention to deadlines. You'll need to get started a whole year before you actually want to enroll. Candidates are usually interviewed in the Fall, Winter and Spring before the Fall they will enter school. So if you wanted to go in 2018, you would need to start your application process in the Spring or Summer of 2017. You can find an application timeline and deadlines at www.aamc.org under the applicants section.

Allopathic medical schools use a central application service called AMCAS (American Medical College Application Service). You do one application and then choose the schools it will be sent to. There is a $160 processing fee and then a separate $36 fee for each additional school. You can get more information on applying at www.aamc.org/students/applying/amcas/.

Writing your personal statement is a major part of your med school application. The admissions boards will be reading thousands of statements. You'll need an attention grabbing first sentence to make your statement stand out from the rest. The other things that schools will be looking for are academics. You'll have to say something that shows that you can handle high-level scientific thoughts and the course load that you'll be faced with in medical school. You can talk about research experiences you've had or something you found fascinating in an upper-level science course.

Any school worth their salt is going to be looking for well-rounded individuals. What does that mean? It means they want someone who has a life outside of school and knows how to interact with people. They'll want to hear a little bit about the sport you played or the club or social group to which you belonged. You can explain how it helped you to understand different kinds of people or helped you develop leadership skills.

Have someone who knows you read your personal statement before you submit it. I thought mine was awesome until my friend read it. She reminded me of some things I had left out, like some of the research I had done.

Chances are, you didn't get a letter of recommendation from your professors immediately after taking their class. So unless you developed a deep personal relationship with them during the class, it's possible they will have difficulty remembering you and all your glowing attributes. Help them out. In addition to your cover letter telling them what kind of letter you need, where they should send it and any deadlines, give them a copy of your rèsumè with a small picture of you attached. Don't be shy about following up with a phone call or an office visit if your deadline is approaching and your recommender has not completed your letter. Don't forget to send thank you letters to your recommenders as well.

If your college or university has a pre-medical office and or a pre-medical advisor, get to them as soon as you think you may be interested in medical school. They can save you a lot of time, money and heartache in the realm of test prep and applications. They might also have an in on the sweet research opportunities, summer programs or physician shadowing programs. My pre-med advisor at Howard University was the incomparable Dr. Georgiana Aboko-Cole (may she rest in paradise). She was with me from day one of my pre-freshman program, all the way through college. She gave me a reality check about my piss-poor grades from the first semester of freshman year. Dr. Aboko-Cole let me know, in no uncertain terms, that it just would not be acceptable. She expected more from me. I started out with a 2-point-I-can't-tell-you GPA. I spent the rest of my time at Howard working hard to try to resurrect my GPA.

You can major in anything you want and still go to medical school, but no one can get around taking the prerequisites. Here are some of the basic prerequisites that most med schools require:

- Biology
- Chemistry (general and organic)
- Physics
- English

Check the Association of American Medical Colleges (AAMC) website for specifics on certain schools that you're interested in. Some also require Calculus or advanced science courses. If you check the requirements early, it will be easier to plan what classes you need to take.

If you want to interview early, get your application in early. Most schools start interviewing candidates in the Fall. That being said, I interviewed with Howard University College of Medicine in April, which is pretty late. What's interesting is that a lot of people in my late interview group ended up being in my class. Some medical schools offer an Early Decision Program (EDP). You can use this program if you are interested in one particular school and want to find out if you'll be admitted before applying to other schools. The school will let you know their decision by October 1. If you don't get in, you will still have time to apply to other schools.

There are several different funding sources for medical school. There are student loans, scholarships, military programs and the National Health Service Corps (NHSC). I paid for my med school education using federal student loans. Luckily, I had a full scholarship for undergrad, so my total debt was not that huge in the grand scheme of things. If I had it to do over again, I would have applied for an NHSC scholarship. However, at the time I didn't know that I would be going into primary care. I did get into an NHSC loan repayment program after finishing residency, but more about that later. I considered a military scholarship, but I changed my mind when I found out about the different places they could send you. But the military may be a good choice for you. You can look into it by doing an online search for the Health Professions Scholarship Program (HPSP). National Medical Fellowships are for underrepresented minorities. You can find out more about them at www.nmfonline.org. There are some small scholarships that exist through corporations, alumni and other benefactors. Check with the alumni association and the financial aid office at the medical school that accepts you. They should be able to give you some direction.

If you don't mind moving to another country for med school, you should check out ELAM. ELAM is the Latin American School of Medicine in Havana, Cuba. Cuba has one of the best medical systems in the world. Full scholarships are available if you agree to work in an underserved area after graduation. Go to medicc.org for more information about the program and how they transition you into a U.S. residency and medical career. Prospective U.S. students can apply through Pastors for Peace.

IFCO/Pastors for Peace
418 W. 145th Street
New York, NY 10031
www.ifconews.org

Another popular medical school in the Caribbean is Ross University School of Medicine in Dominica. You can find out more about them at www.rossu.edu/medical -school. Tulane University's Pre-Health Advising center has a nice article about International and Off-Shore

Medical Schools at tulane.edu/advising/prehealth/how/ international.cfm. One of the resources they list is the International Medical Education Directory (IMED). This is a searchable list of foreign medical schools. Go to www.faimer.org/resources/imed.html to get started.

Interview Tips

1. Review your own rèsumè and personal statement (remind yourself why you're awesome).

2. If you have any grades or test scores that aren't stellar, be ready to explain them. Briefly tell what happened and what you learned from it. Spin it into a positive.

3. Try to get a friend or professor to mock interview you so you can get used to talking about yourself.

4. Limit yourself to one alcoholic drink if there is a pre-interview dinner or luncheon.

5. Dress conservatively (blue or black suit).

6. Arrive early.

7. Pray, meditate—whatever you do to relax yourself.

8. Ask questions. You need to find out if you like the place.

9. Hang out and talk to some students after the interview.

10. Make sure you get your interviewer's email or "snail" mail so that you can send them a thank you note or email.

CHAPTER 5

This Is a Test…
This Is Only a Test

You may not control all the events that happen to you,
but you can decide not to be reduced by them.

MAYA ANGELOU

Standardized testing is part of life for anyone who is, or is becoming a doctor. There is a test for every phase before you can move to the next level. It starts with the MCAT (Medical College Admissions Test). It is given several times a year, but make sure you pay attention to the application deadlines so that you don't miss the date for the test you want to take. Also give some thought to taking it early, so that you will have time to take it again if you aren't happy with your score. The MCAT is changing from the original MCAT to the MCAT 2015. The organization and scoring of the exam is different now. According to the AAMC website, "The total score ranges from 472 to 528. The midpoint is 500." The new sections include:

- Biological and Biochemical Foundations of Living Systems Section
- Chemical and Physical Foundations of Biological Systems Section
- Psychological, Social, and Biological Foundations of Behavior Section
- Critical Analysis and Reasoning Skills Section

Different schools have different minimum MCAT score requirements. You can check services.aamc.org/30/msar/home for each school's requirements. Go to www.aamc.org/students/applying/mcat/mcat2015/administration/ for information on the testing calendar, fees and test prep materials for the new version of the exam. Hopefully, you have great grades. If you don't, a high MCAT score can offset this. I did okay on the MCAT, but I probably would have been considered by more schools if my score had been higher.

I consider the USMLE (United States Medical Licensure Exam) to be the big one. You cannot get licensed to practice medicine in the United States without passing all 3 steps of this exam. USMLE Step I is usually taken between the second and third year of medical school. Some medical schools require you to pass it before you can move from your academic years (1 and 2) to your clinical years (3 and 4). My school had this requirement.

Here's a secret: I failed Step I two times. I was upset the first time it happened. I was absolutely devastated the second time. I was only a few points away from passing each time. I had to swallow my pride in order to get past this hurdle. The first time I failed the test, I was still in school. They allowed me to take one research class and spend the rest of my time studying. After my second failed attempt, I had to take the entire spring semester off. I was sent to Rutherford, New Jersey for an intensive three month test prep course. Initially, I was ashamed because everyone knew about it. However, I ended up learning a lot there. I learned about my test-taking fears and how to overcome them. I also learned a lot of medical facts and test-taking skills that would allow me to finally conquer the test. I kept motivational stories and quotes on my wall while I was there. This had been a habit of mine since undergrad. One of the stories was a magazine article about Chris Gardner. If you don't know who Chris Gardner is, you might know the movie about his life, "The Pursuit of Happyness." He kept going despite many obstacles, including homelessness. I wasn't homeless, but I could certainly refocus myself as he had many times over. I pulled myself up and channeled all my energies toward the goal of passing this test.

When I came back, I was nervous but prepared. I was nervous because I knew this was my last chance. If I failed again, that would be it for me. I would be put out of school. Thank God for miracles though. The third time was the charm! I passed and re-entered school that Fall.

What's funny is that I haven't had any problems with standardized testing since then. There have been several tests that I was able to pass without difficulty. I took the USMLE Step II, which I had to pass to graduate. Step III I took just before the end of residency in order to obtain a medical license. Then there was my board certification for Family Practice. By that point, I was an experienced test-taker. I actually had fun with the patient scenarios part of the exam! I'm pretty proud of that certification. All doctors who practice medicine in the United States have to be licensed, but not all are board certified. After everything that I went through with test-taking, it's kind of a badge of honor for me. Hopefully, you won't have the same kind of struggle. Here are some exam resources for you to help you get your mind right:

- MCAT: www.aamc.org/students/applying/mcat/ mcat2015/administration/
- USMLE Step I: www.usmle.org, www.usmleworld.com, www.nbme.org
- USMLE Step II CK and CS: www.usmle.org, www.usmleworld.com, www.nbme.org
- USMLE Step III: www.usmle.org, www.usmleworld.com, www.fsmb.org
- Board Certification Exams: www.abms.org, www.fsmb.org

CHAPTER 6

What Should I Do If I Don't Get In?

When God closes a door,
somewhere He opens a window.

THE SOUND OF MUSIC

Don't fall apart. It happens. One of the greatest physicians I have ever met (we'll discuss Dr. Leffall in a later chapter) did not get into medical school on his first try. However, I did not feel great when I got a mailbox full of rejection letters. I was questioning God, questioning myself and questioning what direction to go in next. I did not have a plan B. My mother suggested that I apply to graduate school as a backup. But I knew I did not want to go to graduate school. I decided to get a job and try again the following year.

I found a job as a seventh grade Earth Science teacher at a school in Washington, D.C. I also registered for a Biochemistry class at G.W. University. The school where I taught was located in an area of D.C. known as Simple City. Simple City was a rough neighborhood, to say the least. The school building itself looked like a prison, a huge off-white building with small windows, sitting on top of a hill. The initial thing I thought was weird was the metal detector at the main entrance. The school only went from kindergarten to eighth grade, but I would soon find out why they needed it. Some of these kids were drug dealers, had been involved in violence and some even had parole officers. It was like a scene from the movie, *Lean on Me*. Don't get me wrong though, I had some incredibly brilliant kids in my classes. There was one kid who was interested in Astronomy, another in Architecture, and yet another made it to the citywide spelling bee. I was an inexperienced teacher, but I tried my best to give the kids experiences they had never had. We germinated bean seeds in different kinds of soil and had a contest to see whose team could grow the tallest stalk. We made layered brownies with each layer representing the Earth's strata. I had the kids do reports on Black inventors and scientists. I wanted them to get inspired. I wanted them to be able to get out of their current situation. Each day was filled with frustration. These kids were way behind grade levels in reading, math and just general reasoning skills. Some of the kids had been passed on because they were too old to stay in the same grade for yet another year. Others had been promoted because the teacher they had did not want to deal with having that child in their class again. I heard one teacher say this, and I can't say that I blame them—there were so many behavioral problems. Trying to teach there was like beating your head against a brick wall. One day, I got so fed up and angry that I started to cry. One girl asked me, "Why are you even trying? Don't you know you're in Simple City?"

The kids fully expected me to leave. I heard that the teacher before me went out to lunch one day and never came back. Even though some days I did not know what I was doing there, I was determined to stay until the end of the year. Kids threatened to vandalize my car, they threatened me physically, but I was never really scared. I felt sorry for them more than anything else. One kid asked me, "What would you do if I put a gun to your head? Would you change my grade?" I told him, "You would just have to kill me. I would rather die than give someone a grade they didn't deserve." Kids were always bucking up to me, standing over me as if they were going to do something. I warned them early and often, "You might be bigger than me, you might even be able to beat me, but if you ever touch me, you'll never forget you've been in a fight with Ms. Hagans." That would become a self-fulfilling prophecy.

There was one particular girl in my class who was bigger than me, and had an attitude to match. She came into class late, and we had words. She punched me in the face. I can't remember what happened for the next few seconds, it's like I blanked out or something. The next thing I knew, they were pulling me off of the girl. The school administrators asked me if I wanted to press charges. I didn't. I just wanted to be done with the whole situation. I finished out the school day and went home. This is how I know God loves me…when I got home from school that day, my acceptance letter for Howard University College of Medicine was in the mailbox. The lesson in that is this:

Sometimes God allows drastic things to happen to move you in the right direction.

If the kids had been nice and well-behaved, I might still be a teacher today. But I wasn't supposed to stay there. Also, I was able to live on the money I made from teaching during my first year of medical school. I had been living with my parents, so the money that I would have spent in rent was accumulating in my bank account. The other lesson is that you don't ever know the reason for your so-called sufferings, sometimes it isn't even about you. Sometimes God is using you as an example, an inspiration or motivation for someone else. Who knows what my former students will become. Maybe this experience I had was for you. An example to prove you should never give up. Your dreams could be right around the corner or in the mailbox.

Now don't you all run out and apply to be teachers! You have other options if you don't get into medical school on the first try. Post-baccalaureate programs are designed for people who decided they wanted to become doctors after they've already graduated from college. Some people have majored in something non-science related; some people have had whole other careers. These programs allow people to take the prerequisite courses that they need to apply to medical school. You may be able to enter certain post-bac programs to beef up your GPA and make you a better candidate. Go to services.aamc.org/postbac to research programs.

If you have already taken the prerequisites, then you'll have to find some sort of meaningful employment while you wait. What is considered meaningful? Admissions committees are going to want to see that you did something related to science, medicine or some humanitarian effort. The National Institutes of Health (NIH) has a post-baccalaureate intramural research training award (post-bac IRTA/CRTA) that is focused on biomedical research. You can find out if there are any projects that interest you, if you're eligible and how to apply by going to www.training.nih.gov/programs/postbac_irta. Other research opportunities can be found on the following sites:

- www.pathwaystoscience.org
- www.hopkinsmedicine.org/graduateprograms/ prep.cfm
- Sackler.tufts.edu/Academics/Non-degree-programs/ Post-baccalaureate-internships

AmeriCorps is a corporation for national and community service. You can go to the website nationalservice.gov/programs/AmeriCorps/Im-ready-serve for more information. Some other volunteer opportunities could be found at soup kitchens, homeless shelters, free clinics or the American Red Cross. Check out www.gapmedics.com and www.studyabroad .com for international medical shadowing opportunities.

CHAPTER 7

A Wide Open Firehose (The First Two Years)

On more than one occasion, I have decided
that I was not tired and got my arse up
and did some work. Tired is a decision.

TWEETED BY POET KOMPLEX, @MRKEEPONMOVING

The thing that surprised me the most when I arrived at Howard University College of Medicine was how brilliant everyone was. It was kind of weird to be in a class where everyone had been at the top of their class wherever they came from. Some of these people were so smart, their sheer brain power could melt you. Even though it intimidated me at first, it was a challenge that I needed. It challenged my study patterns and my work ethic. It kept me motivated. It reminds me of a quote I saw on a T-shirt once: "*Somebody somewhere is practicing, and when you meet them in one on one competition, they'll beat you.*" In order to get there, stay there and graduate, you have to give it everything you've got. You have to be willing to give up TV, miss movies, parties, clubs and even time with family in order to be successful in medical school. As one of my favorite motivational speakers Eric Thomas always says, "Do not be outworked."

Just the other day, someone was asking me about medical school. She asked, "Was it hard?" It wasn't hard in the sense that the information was difficult to understand. The sheer volume of information you are expected to learn, master and recall on demand is what makes it hard. The best explanation I've heard is that medical school is like trying to take a sip of water from a wide open firehose. It can be overwhelming, but people do it every day. They figure out how to get all the reading, studying and reviewing done. Why not you? What I found worked for me was having a detailed schedule. You may not be as obsessive as me, but I had a calendar broken down into hours. I had all activities scheduled to the tee. It was even color coded. I put everything on that calendar. I scheduled when and what I was going to study, down to what pages I was going to read between 8 and 9 PM. I even wrote down when I was going to eat and sleep!

I can't really remember disliking any courses during those first two years. But I do remember sleeping through a lot of Neuroscience. I guess I wasn't that interested in it because it wasn't what I was planning on going into. But here's the caveat: you don't know what you're going to end up doing. I started out wanting to be an obstetrician, then a surgeon. Now I am a Family Practice physician. You want to be prepared for any scenario. You never know what little nugget of information you pull from your med school mind could end up saving a patient's life. You've got to have something in your mental rolodex to reach back for.

I had a patient that came to me once with swelling in his joints. The confusing thing was that he was too young to have arthritis. Also, the problem would move from one joint to another. One day it would be his knee that was painful and swollen; the next day it would be his elbow. I started digging through my med school memory, trying to recall what could cause a migratory arthritis. I suddenly remembered that gonorrhea or chlamydia could cause this. The patient denied any possibility of this, but I told him I was going to test him anyway. He came up positive. I referred him to an Orthopedic surgeon to draw some fluid off of his joint before I treated him for the STD (sexually transmitted disease). The results from the joint aspiration came back a few days later and his joint fluid was full of white blood cells, a sign of infection. I'm glad I was paying attention on the day that was taught, and I'm sure that patient is glad too! There was a Radiology professor that I had who always said, "No learning is wasted." I'm a true believer in that now.

I think Anatomy Lab was the class I liked the most. The human body is so intricately constructed and awe-inspiring. The other great thing about it was that wearing scrubs and wielding a scalpel made me feel like a surgeon. One of the most memorable times was when we worked on the head and neck. We were having a lot of fun with the dental students who joined us for that part of the class. Our cadaver's face had been covered up until that point. It was easy to dissect the rest of the body, but cutting into a person's face proved difficult and emotional. Our cadaver was a heavy set man with thick, rope-like muscles. We were trying to expose the neck muscles for a particular assignment, but my group was having a hard time. Our professor, Dr. Aziz, came by our table to find out what was wrong. As he donned some gloves he announced, "In order to make an omelet, you must first crack a few eggs." Crack! With one swift motion, he had snapped our cadaver's neck. I learned a valuable lesson that day. Never be afraid to do what you need to do in order to obtain the desired result.

I would be remiss if I didn't mention Dr. Jackson, our Pathology professor. God rest his soul. Dr. Jackson was old school, and the sweetest person you would ever want to meet. He took great pleasure in showing us diseased organs and teaching us about what made them that way. He would also tape himself and students going through the different stations for us to use as a visual study guide. He always played an old tape recording of Duke Ellington's "Take the A Train" at the end of it. He wanted us to all succeed in his class, and in life.

> *Never be afraid to do what you need to do in order to obtain the desired result. If you feel a certain way about it, get over it. Get the job done.*

Earlier in this chapter, I talked about all the things I gave up for medical school. One thing I never gave up was church and time with God. I had to feed my spiritual self, or I never would have made it. I went to Rankin Chapel on the main campus on most Sundays. Then some classmates and I discovered the 6 PM service at Reid Temple A.M.E. It didn't hurt that the preacher was a college acquaintance and they served dinner before church. We went faithfully. I also took breaks from studying to read devotional books and the

Bible. There was a small group of students at the school that held a weekly Bible study. I listened to a lot of inspirational music during that time as well. One song I loved was the Mariah Carey and Whitney Houston song from "The Prince of Egypt" movie soundtrack. It basically sums up the whole med school experience.

We are not afraid, although we know there's much to fear. We were moving mountains long before we knew we could. There can be miracles, when you believe. Though hope is frail, it is hard to kill. Who knows what miracles you can achieve? When you believe, somehow you will.

You will when you believe.

CHAPTER 8

A Hands-on Approach
(The Clinical Years)

Eat when you can, sleep when you can,
read when you can, pee when you can
and stay the *bleep* away from the pancreas.

UNKNOWN

One of the best times in a medical student's life is the beginning of third year. This is when the completely academic part is over and you get to put what you learned into practice. You and your bright-eyed classmates are unleashed on the hospital and clinics and their unsuspecting patients. You don your short white coat, loaded down with all your medical instruments, pens, the pharmacopoeia and the definitive guide for whatever rotation you're on and show up brimming with excitement. Then reality sets in. Your attending, the doctor in charge, singles you out for some questions you don't know the answer to. Guess what? You realize that you're still going to have to study. In addition to studying, you'll be seeing patients, making hospital rounds and taking calls. Oh, by the way, there will be a test at the end.

I liked something about every rotation during medical school. Some of my favorites were Internal Medicine, Pediatrics and Surgery. I liked Internal Medicine because there were so many interesting cases. It was like doing detective work when a patient came in with seemingly unrelated symptoms and you had to find out what was wrong with them.

From Addison's disease to spontaneous bacterial peritonitis, I soaked it up like an ever-absorbent information sponge. The intelligence and finesse of the chief residents and attendings was truly something to see. There was one Internal Medicine Attending named Dr. Frederick. He was a tall, handsome, no-nonsense, West Indian man who expected you to be thorough at all times. I swear this man could merely sniff the air in a hospital room and tell that the patient was in kidney failure. I'm not on that level, but I learned to pay attention to every detail.

Each word, physical exam finding and even an odor could be the key to unlocking a patient's problem.

The attending that we loved and feared the most was Dr. LaSalle D. Leffall, Jr. I don't mean fear in the sense that we were afraid of him. On the contrary. We reverenced him, wanted to be perfect for him. You see, Dr. Leffall was a living legend. It was rumored that he had dated Lena Horne. It was a fact that he had been in the last HUCM class taught by Dr. Charles Drew, the blood bank pioneer. In 1978, he became the first black president of the American Cancer Society. In 1979, he became the first black president of the American College of Surgeons. He was a big deal! Dr. Leffall loved teaching. He wanted to make sure we were ready for the world. He quizzed us endlessly on the causes of an acute abdomen. He was a stickler for grammar and spelling in any written report. I still think of him to this day when I get ready to spell guaiac or ophthalmology. In those days, Dr. Leffall must have been in his seventies. What was amazing was that he was still operating! Regularly. He wasn't stooped over either. He was straight-backed, clear-eyed and utterly brilliant. We twenty-somethings had to struggle to keep up with him. Talk about longevity. We all wanted to be like him when we grew up.

By the time fourth year rolled around, I had my sights firmly set on surgery. I even took extra surgery rotations to learn more and to get myself noticed. For us, the application process was starting all over again: letters of recommendation, interviews, etc. Then Match Day arrived. Match Day is a day in March when all fourth year medical students in the United States find out where they will go for residency. It is kind of like the NFL draft in that you go to whatever team picks you. What happens is that you list the programs in the order that you like them and they list the candidates in the order that they like, and the computer spits out a match. There's a big ceremony and everyone opens an envelope that tells them where they are going. I did not match. It happens sometimes. Luck of the draw. Sometimes the program that you wanted the most did not want you and vice versa. I would have to participate in the scramble. That process is where students who didn't match and residencies with open slots try to find the right match for them. It's a grueling day that consists of a lot of calling, faxing, praying and hoping. I finally matched with a Preliminary Surgery Program in Roanoke, Virginia. I was so excited! Little did I know what I was in for.

CHAPTER 9

The Wild Blue Yonder (To Residency and Beyond)

Every morning in Africa, a gazelle wakes up.
It knows it must outrun the fastest lion or it will be killed.
Every morning in Africa, a lion wakes up. It knows it must
run faster than the slowest gazelle, or it will starve.
It doesn't matter whether you're the lion or a gazelle;
when the sun comes up, you'd better be running.

CHRISTOPHER MCDOUGALL

Residency begins with internship, your first year of training. You get to be introduced to the wonderful world of pag-
ing, where every nurse, senior resident, attending and switch-
board operator in your hospital has access to you twenty-four
hours a day. It is Murphy's Law that it will beep with some
emergency just before you get ready to take a bite of that
food you've been waiting for all day. You are back to being the
lowest man on the totem pole. Every nasty, difficult or boring
job is yours to do. Why? Because crap rolls downhill. That's
the PG way of telling you what my chief resident told me.

I did my internship at Carilion Roanoke Memorial
Hospital in Roanoke, Virginia. The hospital was set in the
side of a mountain in one of the blandest towns that I had
ever visited. Prior to that, I had considered myself a person
who could adapt to living anywhere. Now I know that I'm a
city girl. At that time, Roanoke had no international restau-
rants that I could find. They rolled up their sidewalks at
around five o'clock. From my estimation, the population was
about 90% white. Buffalo Wild Wings was the most happen-
ing place in town. Not that it would have mattered if there

had been someplace to go, I spent most of my time at the hospital. The little bit of time that I was at home was usually spent sleeping. I fell asleep unintentionally on many days, only to wake up and find that I had left the door unlocked. In that way, it was good that the town was so like Mayberry. There were some days when I would get home from being on call for 24 hours and even the thought of making a sandwich was just too much. I figured if I just went to sleep, I wouldn't know I was hungry!

The daytime was relatively normal at the hospital, with lots of scheduled surgeries and rounding. However, when nighttime came, it seemed like all hell would break loose. I would come to know the true meaning of Dr. Leffall's signature phrase, "equanimity under duress." Carilion was a Level I Trauma Center. This meant they had a trauma surgeon and a neurosurgeon who could put you back together if you had a severed limb, your ATV rolled over you, or your car got smashed between two tractor trailers. The hospital had a helipad, and patients were flown in from miles around for every kind of accident you can imagine. There was a bed in the call room available to me, but most nights it went untouched. Between the traumas and the surgical emergencies on the floor, I didn't have time to sleep. My chief residents were hot, but Grey's Anatomy this was not. I never understood how the characters on that show had the time or energy for all those shenanigans!

The trauma that affected me the most was a young girl who had allegedly been shot by her boyfriend. She was basically dead on arrival, but we tried like hell to revive her. They had already been performing CPR in the field and we continued it once she got there. As with all traumas, we cut her clothes off to expose all of her injuries.

I still remember her puffy, olive green jacket with the fur around the hood, riddled with bullets and soaked with her blood.

The residents usually ran the traumas alone, but suddenly the attending was there with the rib spreaders. He was going to crack her chest. I will never forget the sound of bones cracking as he cranked the rib spreader wider. He lifted her small heart out of her chest and began to pump it in his hand. It seemed like we worked on her for an eternity, but it was of no use. One of the residents noticed that she had air bubbles in the veins of her heart. The time of death was called. The aftermath in that room was like something from a horror movie. There was blood and used equipment everywhere. We had done all that we could do.

My training from Howard came into play one night on the floor. I had been paged continuously during a trauma about a man upstairs who was bleeding from his groin wound. Apparently, he had surgery earlier that day and something was going wrong. The nurses had tried applying direct pressure. They tried sandbagging the wound, but nothing seemed to help. When I arrived to the room, the man was lying in bed in a pool of his own blood. I examined the wound, which was slowly leaking blood down the side of his hip. I gathered some materials and went to work, trying to find the source of the bleeding. I mopped the area with some gauze. What they had worked on earlier that day seemed intact. Then I saw it: the open ends of a small vein, persistently oozing blood. I needed to tie the ends off. I made several attempts, but I could not see what I was doing. The wound was filling with blood too quickly, faster than I could mop it up. I always thought the residents were hazing us as medical students, making us tie surgical knots with our eyes closed. Or having to tie a knot on a hook that was down in a hole on a surgical practice board. Well, I needed all of those skills that night. I prayed, threw the stitch, and tied the knot blindly. Then, just as suddenly as it had started, the bleeding stopped! Thank you God! Thank you Howard University College of Medicine!

As the end of the year neared, I had to decide what I was going to do. After all, this was a one year preliminary surgery internship, not a permanent five year spot. I still wanted to be a surgeon, even after the beating I had taken that year. I applied to several surgery positions, but I had my heart set on Brooklyn Hospital Center. Two of my med school classmates were there, and I knew they would put in a good word for me. I loved it when I visited: the people, the program, the hospital and the neighborhood. So you can imagine my devastation when they didn't choose me. I would have to scramble again. My mind went back to a conversation I had with an attending surgeon one night. She told me that she thought

Family Practice was more suited for the kinds of things I was interested in, like Doctors Without Borders and other medical missions. So, I called some Family Practice programs. There was a program in Portsmouth, Virginia that seemed interested in me. As fate would have it, one of my Howard classmates was there. This was someone who I had started out with, but had moved ahead of me due to my test-taking issues. Thank God she remembered me! They chose me. I'd be heading to the Tidewater area at the end of June.

This program was the antithesis of the surgery program. It was very low key and nice. The residents were happy and semi well-rested. It seemed like I had worked nonstop when I was a surgery resident, and the slower pace was a welcome change. There was a lot more clinic and teaching time built in and the attendings were more laid back. They were knowledgeable and friendly. It reminded me of some of the movie doctors I had loved like Doc Hollywood or Patch Adams. Some even did home visits. This was where I belonged. This was the kind of doctor I could excel at being. I was flattered when I was chosen as Intern of the Year at the end of first year.

Don't get me wrong, there were still emergencies. They were just of a different variety. There were people with massive GI bleeds, patients with dangerously low blood pressures and code blues. "Code blue, MICU. Code blue, MICU." When I heard this, I'd flip out of my call room bed and do a brisk run-walk to the unit. The nurses had already started resuscitating the patient, and in most cases were just humoring me by letting me run the code. We sometimes did chest compressions and sometimes injected said patient with epinephrine and atropine. Most of it was an exercise in futility. CPR does not go the way most people think it does. On TV, most patients survive being coded. In real life, the majority of people do not survive codes. If you can get their heart beating again, it's usually just a temporizing measure, until they code again. It usually keeps going like that throughout the night until their heart gives up, the family tells you to stop, or your shift is over. There was one particularly bad call night when I definitively decided that hospital medicine was not for me.

For the most part, I enjoyed my family medicine residency. I made a lot of friends, learned a lot, and just generally had a good time. The program was like a family. We had potlucks, parties, baby showers, and shared our lives with each other. I became particularly close to one of my fellow residents during second year. The nurses would always confuse us. I made buttons for our white coats. Hers said, "I'm not Dr. Hagans" and mine said, "I'm not Dr. Darden." We co-coordinated the homeless clinic and the clinic for the battered women's shelter that year. It was hard work, but it was definitely rewarding. When third year rolled around, we were chosen to be co-chief residents. We managed the call schedules, handled resident problems and represented the residents at the provider meetings with the attendings. This gave me valuable management skills that I am still using to this day.

I was so busy managing everyone else's life, I forgot to manage my own. The end of the year was nearing and I hadn't found a job yet. I had to get on the good foot. I began calling around to recruiters and looking at job boards to see what I could find. I visited practices in Atlanta, GA and Charlotte, NC. I didn't feel like they were for me. I couldn't seem to find what I wanted close to home. Then someone from a clinic in New Orleans called me. They had gotten my name from an AAFP (American Academy of Family Physicians) job board. They wanted to know if I was interested in interviewing. This was not long after Hurricane Katrina. I remembered an article that my then boyfriend, who is now my husband, had mentioned about the need for police officers and doctors there. I had always wanted to see what it was like to live in New Orleans. I had applied to Xavier University for undergrad, but the scholarship they offered was pretty small, so I declined their offer. The interview that I had with the New Orleans clinic went well. I liked the place and people, so I decided to give it a try.

CHAPTER 10

Laissez bon Temps Rouler! (Let the Good Times Roll!)

Anything that stops you from building
your purpose is bondage.

T.D. JAKES

In June of 2008, I graduated from Family Practice residency, ready for the world. Over the summer I spent time with friends and family, relaxed and tried to get ready to move. In August, my boyfriend and I packed up our belongings and started the two day drive to New Orleans, Louisiana. We had not intended to drive, but we got taken by some unscrupulous movers. We had to make the decision at the last minute. I slept most of the way, like I usually do on long drives. I woke up when we were getting to the North Carolina-South Carolina border because the moving truck was swaying back and forth. I knew my boyfriend had been having trouble keeping the truck straight because we were towing my car on a trailer behind us. But this time, it was due to the wind. Then he says to me, "Look in your rearview mirror. Does that look like a funnel cloud to you?" Indeed it was a funnel. There was a tornado behind us, and it was gaining ground. We turned off on the nearest exit, trying to get out of its path. Luckily, the South of the Border rest stop was right there. We parked the truck in between two buildings and jumped out, looking for shelter. We decided against the glass-walled arcade and ran into a low-lying stone building that was a Mexican restaurant. No sooner than we got inside, the tornado arrived and began pummeling the area with wind and rain. Thank God we made it, but was this a bad omen? Only time would tell.

We finally made it to New Orleans after stopping at my future sister-in-law's house in Atlanta overnight. We were exhausted when we got there and just flopped on the inflatable mattress, leaving the rest of the things in the truck. In the following days, we unpacked and tried to get adjusted to life in Louisiana. The air condition in our apartment wasn't working properly, so it was hotter than two hell fires. A few days before I was supposed to start working, Hurricane Gustav veered towards the Gulf Coast. Evacuating wasn't mandatory, but I decided to leave anyway. I caught a flight to my parent's house in Maryland. I watched the news coverage on TV as Gustav battered New Orleans. I returned a few days later. There was damage, but nowhere near the amount of damage that Hurricane Katrina had caused. I was relieved. The only problem was that the roof of the clinic where I was supposed to start working had caved in. I'd have to start work in another building that the owners were renting across town. The place that I thought I would be working was within walking distance of our apartment in a nice New Orleans suburb. The other office was on the West Bank and in the hood. I'd have to make the best of it.

There were other providers in the practice I joined (another doctor and two nurse practitioners), but they would be working elsewhere. This location was going to be my baby to rock. I knew how to manage people from my experiences as a chief resident. Managing myself was a different matter. Being fresh out of school, I wanted to double-check what I was doing. I used the AAFP website a lot, looking up management guidelines for different conditions. I wanted to make sure I was doing things right. Because of this, it took me a long time to see patients. This would get better over time.

The thing that I liked best about this practice was that they had a Ryan White grant. So in addition to being the bread and butter primary care, I got to take care of a panel of HIV patients. They had frequent appointments, lab and social work visits, so I got to know them well. These patients, along with the other patients in the neighborhood were fiercely loyal. A lot of them had never had a doctor to really listen to them and explain things to them. I cried when I had to leave the practice later. I won't go into detail about why I left, but let's just say that the management and I could not see eye-to-eye.

This brings me to another important point: scrutinize your contract. I know you're happy to have your first job as a full-fledged doctor. I know you're excited to be making more money than you've ever made in your life. But listen to me, read it very carefully before you sign. If you don't understand it, get a lawyer to read it. If you don't have a lawyer and can't afford to get one, at least have someone who is more knowledgeable about contracts than you are to look it over. What are you looking for?

- Salary comparable to other starting salaries in the area
- Benefits (Health, Dental, Life Insurance, Retirement Plan)
- Length of service expected
- Expectations or duties involved
- Non-compete clause

I say this because I was not paying attention when I signed my contract. Thankfully, there was no non-compete clause. Physician employers usually put this in contracts to keep you from leaving with all of their patients and setting up shop down the street. I was in New Orleans partially due to the Greater New Orleans Health Service Corps. They had already given me over $100,000 towards my student loans. Because of this, I had to stay in New Orleans for three years total. New Orleans really isn't that big. If I had signed a non-compete clause, I would have been up a creek without a paddle.

That brings me to Common Ground Health Clinic. It was a community clinic not far from where I was working. I had seen their newsletters and had always secretly wanted to work there. Common Ground was founded in 2005 in post-Katrina New Orleans as a sort of first aid way station. It was staffed by volunteers, nurses, street medics, and do-gooders of all types. They set up in tents outside of the neighborhood mosque. Ladies from the neighborhood cooked for the workers and clinic supplies were whatever they could find. They saved a lot of lives during that time and are still doing so to this day. This was the most unique clinic I had ever seen. They had traditional medicine, herbalists, nutritionists and acupuncture. They also had a kitchen and a community garden. I made the decision to join them in November of 2010, and it is one of the best decisions I have ever made. I learned so much about nutrition, herbs, and "alternative" medicine. I unlearned some

Sometimes a person doesn't need pills. Sometimes they need to be shown what to eat and given support around that.

med school thinking that said you needed to prescribe everyone a medicine.

I discovered my true passion there, preventive medicine and lifestyle modification. It was a joy to work there, seeing patients, working my little plot in the garden, participating in the cooking classes and meeting a lot of interesting people along the way. I was only obligated to stay there for one year to fulfill the grant requirement, but I ended up staying two years because I loved it so much. I also wanted to give them enough time to find a new provider who would be right for the clinic.

I was happy to be going home to begin the next phase of my life, but a little sad to be leaving New Orleans. I would miss the crawfish, gumbo and grilled oysters from Drago's. I would later dream about the apple fritters from Honey Whipped and beignets from the famous Café du Monde. I would always remember the sound of the second lines, the sight of the floats during Mardi Gras and the raucousness of Bourbon Street. But most of all, I would miss the people. The amazing patients, co-workers, friends and church members that I had met during my stay.

CHAPTER 11

"You *Can't* Be the Doctor."

Our deepest fear is not that we are inadequate. Our deepest fear is that we are powerful beyond measure. It is our light, not our darkness that most frightens us. We ask ourselves, who am I to be brilliant, gorgeous, talented, and fabulous? Actually, who are you not to be? You are a child of God. Your playing small does not serve the world. There is nothing enlightened about shrinking so that other people will not feel insecure around you...

MARIANNE WILLIAMSON

O n Election Day in November of 2012, I boarded a plane to Washington Dulles International Airport. I was moving home to be closer to friends and family and to begin working on my dream of owning my own clinic. I had voted early and they were tallying the votes from each district live on TV as I walked through the airport. America was trying to decide if Barack Obama would stay on as President. I almost cried when I drove over the 14th Street Bridge and saw the Washington monument against the nighttime sky. I did not realize until then how much I had missed home.

I had a job lined up with a clinic in Hagerstown, Maryland through a locum tenens company. Locum tenens companies are like temp agencies for doctors. They provide placement services to doctors who are seeking short-term employment. Some people use this service to travel, to try out a new city, to be closer to family, or to transition from one career to another. I was using it for income while I worked on my business plan. It didn't turn out exactly the way I wanted though because I made the mistake of signing on to work five days a week. This clinic was super busy, and I found myself doing more work for them than for myself, even after I got home. I did work on my business plan as much as I could. I also took a few online business related courses while I was there.

One of the problems I had in Hagerstown was the isolation. Even though it was in Maryland, it was still over an hour away from any friends and family. I decided to follow the advice of Rosetta Thurman of happyblackwoman.com and Hill Harper in his book, *The Wealth Cure* and start a mastermind group. A mastermind group is usually made up of a small group of like-minded individuals working together to solve problems and provide each other support. In all that I had read about masterminds, the members tended to become more successful than they would have become on their own. So in January 2013, the Fruition Networking Group was born. I invited a few old friends, who were also black female doctors to join the group. We tried to meet once a month to discuss goals, successes, failures and our experiences being young, black, and female physicians.

One common experience we had was co-workers and patients dismissing us on sight. Could a young black female be a competent physician? Most people were caught off guard by seeing me in the driver's seat. I got (and still get) a lot of questions from patients related to this. Patients say the wildest things:

- Oh, are you the doctor? I thought you were a little girl.
- I thought you were the nurse.

- How old are you?
- Where did you go to school?
- How long have you been a doctor?
- I thought you would be a man.
- Are you new here?
- You can't be the doctor.

People are so used to an actual or mental image of a doctor being an older white male, they are not prepared to see someone who looks like me. But I rarely have a patient who is dissatisfied with my services. On the contrary. A lot of people want to find out how they can change their doctor to me by the time the visit ends. Then I have people who are glad to see me and will whisper in the hallways or the exam room about how proud they are. I saw an older black gentleman once, who by his accent and appearance may have been from Ethiopia. He told me that when he went to college at a predominantly white school, people stared at him "like an animal." He remarked on how far we had come in such a short period of time that so many young black people now had the opportunity to become doctors.

Never let comments like this make you feel insecure. Your degree and license proves this: the place where you were trained and the state where you practice, thought you were competent. Stay strong, look that skeptical patient in the eye, and exude confidence. You can change the face of medicine and the perception of what a doctor is, one patient at a time.

CHAPTER 12

Hope for the Future

I would hate to die and not do
the thing I was born to do.

T.D. JAKES

Becoming a doctor is a lofty goal and there can be a lot of bumps and bruises along the way. It takes a singular focus and incredible determination. I hope that you'll persevere and make it to where you want to be. Get clear on your reason for doing it. Keep that reason in the forefront of your mind. Write it down, make vision boards, and put it on your wall. Then put your nose to the grind and make it happen.

I'm at a point in my life where a lot of people think I have it made. On the contrary. I now feel even more of a desire to push towards my goals. I'm in the process of opening my own office, and it has been a long, tedious process but I'm nearing the end of the preparation. If the Lord says the same, I'll be opening soon! At some point, the entrepreneurial bug bit me and I knew I had to strike out on my own. This mostly came out of a desire to do things differently from traditional medicine. I think Family Medicine docs need to start focusing on lifestyle changes. I'd rather find out what you eat and do to help you make the necessary changes than just pile on more pills. My passion is cooking, gardening, nutrition and overall wellness. I'm working on how to incorporate that into what I do every day.

Don't let anyone pigeon-hole you into a role or position that you know isn't your passion. Not your parents, your friends, your boss, your spouse, your mentor, or anyone. Even if you're good at whatever it is you are doing, it may not be the right path for you. As Eric Thomas says, "you have to give up something good to get to great." Yes, you'll have to pay some dues. But you will soon gain enough experience to strike out on your own, or implement your own ideas where you are. If you don't know what your passion is, check out Rosetta Thurman at

> *If you don't pursue your passions, I think you die a little bit every day.*

happyblackwoman.com or Jullien Gordon at julliengordon. com. They both have some in-depth tools to help you figure out what you want out of life, why you want it and how to get it.

Les Brown gave a speech once where he talked about the graveyard being the richest place in the world. He went on to say that most people die with their dreams still in their hearts. They take businesses, books and ideas to the grave with them. I'm determined not to let this be me. I intend to serve people, change the world and die with no regrets. I want to do everything that God has purposed for me to do.

When I stand before God at the end of my life,

I would hope that I would not have

a single bit of talent left, and could say,

I used everything you gave me.

ERMA BOMBECK

CHAPTER 13

Survival Guide
(Future Doctor Checklist)

Check yourself before you wreck yourself.

DAS EFX FEATURING ICE CUBE

As a busy future doctor, you might not have time to reread this whole book. You can use the lists below to refer to periodically and keep yourself on track. It's divided into stages so you can easily find the tips that you need: Pre-med, Medical School, Residency, and You're a Doctor Now.

Pre-med

1. Make sure being a doctor is what you really want to do (shadow doctors, read their stories, and find out what their lives are like).

2. Try to get good grades in college. If you didn't start out strong, work hard to improve. Don't be afraid to get a tutor or seek help from your professors.

3. Visit the pre-med advisor at your college as soon as you decide you're interested. If your school does not have one, still visit the general advisors' office and tell them about your intentions. They should be able to help you plan your coursework.

4. If your school has a pre-med club, join it. A lot of times they will have speakers, tips and opportunities that are of interest to you.

5. Do some scientific research. Try to work with some-one who has a topic you're interested in. Admissions boards want to see that you have a scientific mind. You could check with the office of the Biology or Chemistry departments at your school, or look online for summer opportunities.

6. Prepare for the MCAT (see the resources section).

7. Check the admissions requirements for the schools you're interested in.

8. Ask for letters of recommendations early. Give your recommenders a rèsumè with a cover letter and a small picture of you attached.

9. Send thank you notes to your recommenders.

10. Write your personal statement.

11. Get a few people who know you to read your personal statement.

12. Apply early.

13. Get a conservative suit or outfit for interviews. By conservative, I mean blue or black in a style that won't shame your entire family. You can express your personal style after you get accepted. You can wear the same out-fit to all of your interviews as long as it's clean.

14. Send thank you notes/emails to the people that inter-view you. They'll be giving their recommendations about you to the admissions board.

15. Wait.
16. Pray.
17. Wait.
18. Pray.
19. Do the happy dance if you're accepted.
20. If at first you don't succeed; try, try again.
21. Apply for financial aid and scholarships.
22. Enjoy your summer! Visit all your friends and family. It may be a long time before you see them again. I'm serious.

Medical School

1. Find a study buddy. You'll need someone to poke and prod you when you get sleepy.
2. If there's no big brother/pal system at your school, try to identify a second year student who can tell you the tricks of the trade (and maybe even give you some old books/study guides).
3. Develop a study schedule and stick to it. Put everything in your calendar and put a time frame on it. Example: Microbiology pages 20–30 from 8–9 PM on Thursday.
4. Don't worry about TV or movies. There was a large chunk of time where I just didn't have time to watch anything recreational. It really will be okay.
5. Try not to destroy your teeth and stomach with junk food, candy and caffeine. Fast food might be a necessary evil, but try to make healthy choices.
6. Don't forget God. Keep going to church, praying, meditating, or whatever your spiritual practice is.

7. Try to review the material that is taught in class on the same day. It will stick better.

8. Mnemonics are your friend. If you can't find one for the set of facts that you're trying to remember, make one up.

9. For your clinical rotations, keep some books or apps handy for random factoids. You can't remember everything. That's why God made the Pharmacopeia.

10. Round early if you have a choice. The earlier it is, the less competition there is for your patient's chart.

11. During fourth year, try to do an extra rotation in the specialty you're interested in. This can be a good source of letters of recommendation for you.

12. Rinse and repeat your med school application tips when applying for residency.
    • Research the programs
    • Get letters of recommendation early
    • Apply early
    • Send thank you notes

Residency

1. Get ready to grind out.

2. Stock your work locker/storage with extra underwear, toiletries and snacks. Get some frozen or canned dinners for home for the days when you are too tired to imagine cooking.

3. Put your bills on auto-pay. You will be too tired to remember to pay them manually.

4. Get a little notebook for call night. You're only one person. Therefore and ergo, you won't be able to save everyone all at once. You'll need to write down the patient's name, room number, problem and the name of the nurse that called you. Check them off as you deal with them. This will help you with morning reports or morning rounds as well.

5. Start rounding early.

6. Document, document, document. If you do or say anything to a patient, write a note. It doesn't necessarily have to be in the SOAP (Subjective, Objective, Assessment and Plan) format, but write something. If you can't prove it, you didn't do it.

7. Unless there is an emergency you can't handle or you don't know what to do, try to get as much information as possible before you call your superior. If you are an intern, then the senior resident on call is your superior. Do not call your attending without speaking with the resident first. Especially in the middle of the night. It's protocol.

8. Read about your patient's conditions. The info will stick better if you have a mental hook to hang it on.

9. Do your homework when applying for after residency jobs. Is the organization in financial trouble? Do they have a high turnover rate? Do they have benefits that include a retirement plan, health insurance, paid vacations? Read your contract carefully. Do they have a non-compete clause that is far reaching? If you do need

to leave and the clause is too broad, you may have to move in order to find new employment.

You're a Doctor Now!

1. Congratulations, you made it!
2. Stay on top of the dates and fees required for renewing your license. Also pay attention to how many Continuing Medical Education (CME) credits you need to maintain licensure. You can get CME online or in person at a dinner or a conference. Conferences tend to be expensive, but you may be able to get your employer to pay for them. You can accumulate a huge amount of credits (usually 15–35) during the span of the conference.
3. Board certification. In the United States, all practicing doctors are licensed, but not all are board certified. Board certification is a feather in your cap. It says that you are up on the latest information concerning your specialty. You can find out more about examination requirements and how to register through the American Board of Medical Specialties website at www.abms.org.
4. Stay on top of your documentation. If you can't prove it, you didn't do it. Most organizations have some sort of requirement about finishing office notes, replying to phone calls and completing prescription refills in a timely fashion. Even if they don't, try to finish those things within 24 hours.

5. Join professional societies. NMA, AMA, the academy for your specialty and the local medical society for your states and city are some options. They can be a valuable source of information on continuing medical education, updated standards of care and networking with other doctors.

6. Value your staff. Be nice to nurses, front desk personnel, social workers and all the people who are there to help you. Ask instead of ordering. People will be more willing to help you if they like you as a person. A disgruntled nurse can ruin your day, week and even your career. Staff who feel respected by you will do anything to make your day easier.

7. Get a life. Medicine isn't the only thing in the world. Now that you're a full-fledged doctor, try to break away a little and start feeding your other interests. Always wanted to visit a certain country, go to a Jazz Fest, take up painting or learn a language? Do it! It is tempting to throw yourself into your new job and become a workaholic, but you don't want to burnout. Try to find some things outside of work that you are passionate about and start living now!

8. Alternative careers. Maybe academic medicine or private practice isn't right for you. There are other types of work that might be right up your alley.

    *   Locum tenens
    *   Community clinics
    *   Doctors Without Borders

- School based clinics
- Consultant
- Lobbyist
- Supervisor for minute clinic
- Telemedicine

CHAPTER 14

Resources

Whenever my environment had failed

to support or nourish me,

I had clutched at books.

RICHARD WRIGHT, *BLACK BOY*

Books for General Knowledge and Inspiration

- *The Delaney Sisters' Book of Everyday Wisdom.* Sarah Delany, A. Elizabeth Delany and Amy Hill Hearth
- *The Purpose Driven Life.* Rick Warren
- *Crush It: Why Now Is the Time to Cash in on Your Passion.* Gary Vaynerchuck
- *The Wealth Cure: Putting Money in its Place.* Hill Harper
- *Think Big: Unleashing Your Potential for Excellence.* Ben Carson
- *The Pact: Three Young Men Make a Promise and Fulfill a Dream.* Sampson Davis, George Jenkins and Rameck Hunt
- *How to Win Friends and Influence People.* Dale Carnegie

Resources for College, Medical School and Residency Application and Preparation

- www.youngdoctorsdc.org
- www.pathwaystoscience.org: Information on scientific experiences for grades K-12, undergraduates, graduate students, post-doctoral students, etc.
- www.ExploreHealthCareers.org: Information on MD and non-MD health careers
- www.petersons.com: Information for high school and college students about preparing for college or grad school admissions, test prep and scholarships
- *Preparing for College Admissions: The Ultimate Guide for Parents and Students.* Carolyn Croom Baker. www.achievementworks.com

- www.future-md.net blog
- *How NOT to Apply to Medical School.* Paul Jung
- *So, You Want to Be a Physician: Getting an Edge in Your Pursuit of the Challenging Dream of Becoming a Medical Doctor.* Edward M. Goldberg
- *On Becoming a Doctor: Everything You Need to Know About Medical School, Residency, Specialization and Practice.* Tania Heller
- medicc.org: Medical Education Cooperation with Cuba at the ELAM (Latin American School of Medicine of Havana, Cuba). Free medical school!!!
- www.aamc.org: Sections for aspiring docs, applicants, med students and residents
- www.aamcorg/students/applying.amcas: American Medical College Application Service. AMCAS processing fee for 2015 is $160 for one school and $36 for each additional school. You can apply for a fee assistance program through the AAMC. If you qualify, you could have AMCAS fees waived and MCAT registration fees reduced. The medical school itself may have a secondary application process and associated fee. This website also has a timeline for application/admission to medical school, under the "applicants" tab. It breaks down what you can do each year of college to prepare.
- www.tmdsas.com: Texas Medical and Dental Schools Application Service

Resources for Medical School Rotations

- MKSAP (Medical Knowledge Self-Assessment Program): mksap.acponline.org
- *Surgery Recall.* Lorne. H Blackbourne, MD FACS
- *Pharmacology Recall.* Anand Ramachandran
- *Bates' Guide to Physical Examination and History Taking.* Lynn Bickley, MD
- Tarascon Pharmacopeia www.tarascon.com: You can download the app but it is still available in a pocket handbook as well.
- Epocrates www.epocrates.com: You can download the app or access it on line.
- www.internetmedicine.com: A listing of some other medical apps (some free, some for a fee)

Resources for New Physicians

- *How to Start a Medical Practice from the Ground Up.* American Academy of Family Physicians
- *The White Coat Investor.* James M. Dahle, MD
- whitecoatinvestor.com blog
- www.kevinmd.com blog
- www.mayoclinic.org: Symptoms, diagnosis, work-up, treatment of diseases
- www.cdc.gov: Treatment guidelines and patient hand-outs
- www.artemismedicalsociety.org
- www.medscape.com

Medical Student Organizations

Both have pre-med chapters as well. These organizations are good for providing leadership experience, volunteer opportunities and even international opportunities. Membership may allow you to find a mentor, grants or scholarships. They also sometimes have discounts on products and services for their members.

- www.amsa.org: American Medical Student Association
- www.snma.org: Student National Medical Association

Research Opportunities

- National Institutes of Health (NIH):
  www.trainin.nih.gov/programs/postbac_irta
- www.hopkinsmedicine.org/graduateprograms/
  prep.cfm
- sackler.tufts.edu/Academics/Non-Degree-Programs/
  Post-Baccalaureate-Internships

Test Prep

- www.aamc.org/students/mcat/registration.html: You can find a location and register for the test on this website. It also gives you a content outline for each section, so you know what to study. There is a self-assessment package available for a fee that will help you find out what your weak areas are. There is also a free practice test available.
- www.petersons.com: Sample MCAT questions

- www.usmleworld.com: You can subscribe to a question bank on this site if you pay a set subscription fee for 30, 60, 90, 180 or 360 days of access. It also gives you an idea about the format of each test.
- www.nbme.org: The National Board of Medical Examiners administers USMLE Step 1, Step 2 CK and Step 2 CS
- www.fsmb.org: The Federation of State Medical Boards has USMLE Step 3 info and instructions for obtaining your medical license.
- *First Aid for the USMLE*. Tao Le and Vikas Bhushan
- www.ecfmg.org: The Educational Commission for Foreign Medical Graduates is where students or graduates of medical schools outside of the United States and Canada can go for information on taking the USMLE Step 1 and 2.

CHAPTER 15

Sample Documents

Sample Cover Letter

This is a sample cover letter for a letter of recommendation request. Deliver this in person, if possible. Don't forget to attach your rèsumè or CV and a small picture of yourself (stapled, scanned or uploaded from your phone).

Jarita Hagans
123 Main Street
St. Louis, Missouri 12345
July 1, 2015

Dr. Jane Doe
104 Campus Drive, Ste 203
St. Louis, Missouri 12345

Dear Dr. Doe,

I was a student in your Molecular Biology class last semester. I am applying to medical school and wanted to ask you to write a letter of recommendation for me. If you are willing to do so, I would greatly appreciate it. Please find my CV attached. Thank you in advance for your help.

Sincerely,

J. Hagans
Jarita Hagans

Sample Rèsumè/CV

Jarita Hagans
123 Main Street
St. Louis, Missouri 12345
(123) 456-7890
MDorBust@hotmail.com

Education

First University	August 2012–present
St. Louis, Missouri	
Western High School	August 2008–June 2012
St. Louis, Missouri	

Certifications

Basic Life Support/CPR	July 2012–July 2014

Leadership Experience

Leader of the Sorority Fundraising Committee	2014–present
Treasurer of the Pre-medical Society	2013–2014
Class Treasurer	2011–2012

Community Involvement

Each One Reach One Tutoring Program	2013 and 2014
Soup Kitchen	2012
AIDS Walk	2012, 2013, 2014

Honors and Awards

The Charles Drew Honors Program	2012–present
The Honor Society	2008–2012

Research Experience

The Effect of Soda on Rat Livers

Molecular Endocrinology Lab   2014

   First University. St. Louis, Missouri

Work Experience

Summer Assistant in Pre-medical Advisory Office   2013

Language Skills

Conversational Spanish

Sample Personal Statement

Delivering pigs on my grandfather's farm is one of the things that sparked my interest in medicine. It started me thinking of delivering human babies and being an obstetrician.

I have always had a natural curiosity for anything related to science, so majoring in Biology was a joy for me. I was especially fascinated by Endocrinology and Physiology. This led me to a summer research opportunity in the Molecular Endocrinology lab at First University. My research was on *The Effect of Sodas on Rat Liver*. We found that cola-like sodas caused apoptosis of liver cells by upregulating IL-8. Hopefully, this data can be extrapolated for human benefit.

I was able to gain a lot of leadership experience through my interactions with various clubs and community organizations in and around the St. Louis area. The treasurer positions that I've held showed me how to manage budgets and allocate resources. Organizing a tutoring program and groups for AIDS walks and the soup kitchens taught me how to work well with different types of people and their personalities.

I knew that I had found the right fit when I shadowed an OB-GYN during my sophomore year. The patient interactions in the clinic were emotionally satisfying. The natural deliveries and the cesarean sections were absolutely exhilarating. The piglet deliveries were no match for this!

In order to be an effective physician, one must be inquisitive, compassionate and dedicated. The education

I've received, as well as my scientific research and community involvement have given me the qualities necessary for the practice of medicine. I believe that I would be an asset to any institution that chooses me. I look forward to matriculating into medical school and making my childhood dream a reality.

Gratitude

God you are everything. You gave me the idea for this book in the wee hours of the morning. That's when you seem to give me all of my most inspired ideas. You are the reason why I wanted to make a living out of serving people. You are the reason I did not go crazy during this journey. You are the reason I was placed upon this earth.

"Before I formed thee in the belly I knew thee; and before though camest forth out of the womb, I sanctified thee, and I ordained thee a prophet unto the nations."
—Jeremiah 1:5

I am so grateful for you, husband. While I was in residency, you brought me chicken sandwiches, umbrellas and company while I was on call at the hospital. You wiped my tears when things didn't go right at my first job. You celebrated with me when things went right after that. You have been my constant companion, chef, supporter, lover and confidant. I love you and thank God for you!

Willie and Mary Hagans, thank you for giving me life and for giving me the tools I needed to be successful in life. Thank you for loving me enough to be firm with me, to discipline me, and for helping me maximize my potential. It is not possible to name everything you have done for me. I love you both, and there's nothing you can do about it!

Hagans, Lewis and Harrell Family. I come from a rich heritage of hardworking people. I have been blessed to be part of a spiritual, loving supportive family throughout my life. I am grateful for the ones who went before me and those that still walk beside me today. I know that my grandparents, Henry and Lenora Harrell & Eula and Bennie Lee Hagans, are resting in paradise. I hope that they are proud of me.

I used to say that I was a member of Matthews Memorial Baptist Church since I was a spark in my father's eye. Even though I no longer attend the church, I am bolstered by the prayers of those people. All of my former pastors, Sunday school teachers and people who just supported me are a huge reason why I am a doctor today. Whenever I thought about giving up along the way, I thought about that verse from a Shirley Caesar song: "The people are depending on you, Shirley. Don't you let them down." I knew that everybody there wanted me to win.

I cannot name all of the friends that have supported me along the way but I will name my oldest and most constant friends: Erin Kirkland Graham and Kevin Neale. I have known them since I was twelve, and they have always believed in everything I wanted to do. "No new friends… we don't feel that….a fake friend where your real friends at? We don't like to do too much explaining. Story stay the same through the money and the fame." —Drake (*Started from the Bottom*)

There are countless teachers, guidance counselors, professors and preceptors who saw fit to pour into me. They taught me, took an interest in me and made sure opportunities came my way. Their leading and teachings helped formed me into the person I am today.

With the way the work day is structured, you end up spending more time with the people you work with than your own family. If you like those people, that is a gift from God. Coworkers who made my work life a joy: Darnell, Dana, Joann, Gabby, Jessica, Anna, Jeannie, Nasha, Meshawn, Lucien, Ndidi, Terri, Candi, Paul, Grover, Carolyn, Randy, Rachel, Amy, Peteh and Lynette.

About the Author

Jarita Hagans is a native of Maryland and a lover of books. She completed her undergraduate and medical school years at Howard University in Washington, D.C. Afterwards, she trained in a surgery internship at Carilion Roanoke Memorial Hospital in Roanoke, Virginia. Eastern Virginia Medical School/Portsmouth Family Medicine is where she received her Family Medicine training. She had the honor of being Intern of the Year and Chief Resident while training there. Operating a clinic for a battered women's shelter and providing medical care for a homeless shelter were two of her favorite projects.

After residency, she practiced in post Hurricane Katrina in New Orleans and developed a love for cooking, gardening and natural remedies. Since moving home, she has worked at medical offices in Washington, D.C, as well as Baltimore and several other cities in Maryland. She is the founder of Zion Family Practice, LLC.

Dr. Hagans has had the pleasure of speaking about healthy eating, lifestyle changes and STD prevention in various schools and churches since 2005. In 2015, she was chosen to speak at the Student National Medical Association Annual Medical Education Conference (SNMA AMEC) in New Orleans, Louisiana. She was a featured participant in "Creating Your Path to Medicine," "Physician Panel: A Day in the Life of a Physician" as well as the Mock Interview and Personal Statement Review workshop. She enjoys motivating and mentoring young people on college preparation and health careers.

Made in the USA
Middletown, DE
15 May 2016